Ja   Carpenter

and   His Friends

NICK BUTTERWORTH

WALKER BOOKS
AND SUBSIDIARIES

Jack is a carpenter.

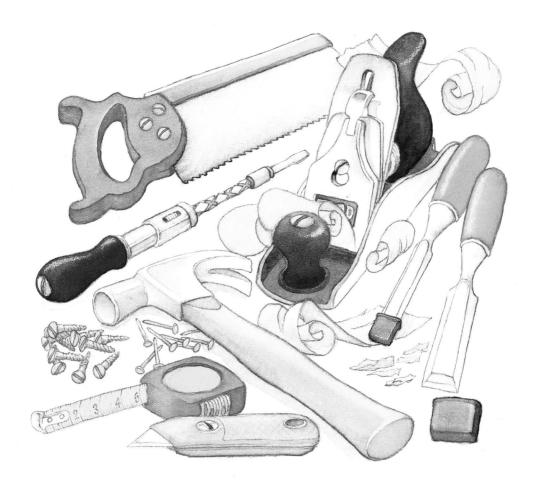

What does he use?

Julie is a paper girl.

What does she bring?

Walter has a toy shop.

What does he sell?

Jenny is a gardener.

What does she use?

Bill is a repair man.

What does he mend?

Sally has a clothes shop.

What does she sell?

Dave is a builder.

What does he drive?

Jane is a cook.

What does she use?

Ron has a hardware shop.

What does he sell?

Amanda is a pilot.